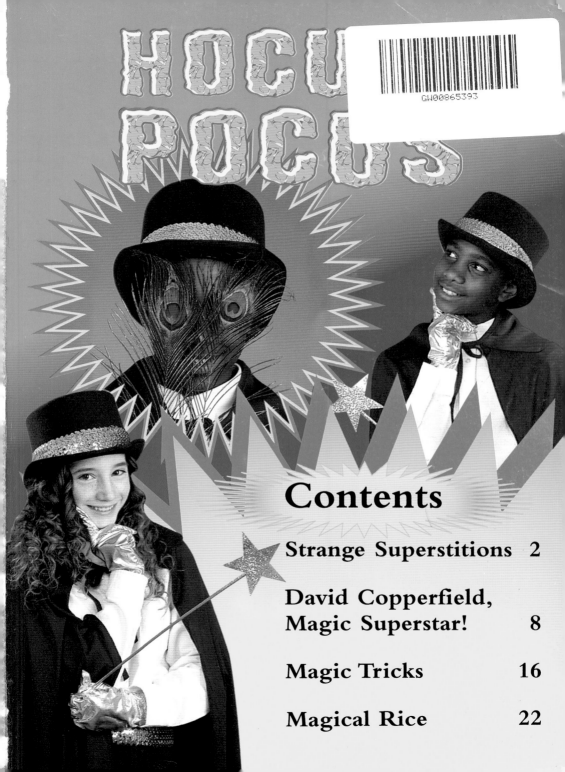

HOCUS POCUS

Contents

Strange Superstitions

Written by Susan Brocker

Illustrated by Chantal Stewart

Do you have a lucky charm?
Do you like to make wishes?
Some people think that things
can make wishes come true.
They say things can bring
good luck or bad luck.
These beliefs are superstitions.

Hang a Horseshoe

A horseshoe is a lucky charm.
Long ago, people said
the moon was lucky.
They said horseshoes
looked like the moon.
So horseshoes were good luck, too.

Always
hang a horseshoe
with its legs up
or all its good luck
will fall out!

3

Walk Under a Ladder? No Way!

People used to say it was bad luck
to walk through a triangle.
A ladder on a wall makes a triangle.
So they said it was bad luck to walk
under a ladder, too.

THE CLUB

Why does this superstition make good sense?

 Don't Spill the Salt!

People once used salt like money.
They said it was bad luck to spill salt.
It was like losing money.
To stop the bad luck,
people would throw salt
over their left shoulder.

Why did
people use salt
like money?

5

Knock on Wood!

Long ago,
people said fairies lived in trees.
People asked the fairies
for good luck
by knocking on a tree
or something made of wood.

Bad-Luck Feathers

Some peacock feathers look
like they have an eye.
People once said
the eye watched you.
They said the eye
gave you bad luck.
What do you think?

Do you have a
superstition?

Wish upon a Star...

People say stars
can make a wish come true.
But it has to be a secret,
or your wish will not come true!

David Copperfield,

SATURDAY, SEPTEMBER 2

The Statue of Liberty – Gone!

Crowds of people saw the Statue of Liberty disappear in front of their eyes.

JULY IV MDCCLXXVI

Magic Superstar!

Written by Janne Galbraith
Illustrated by Kelvin Hawley

Who Did It?

David Copperfield made the Statue of Liberty disappear. David Copperfield is a magician.

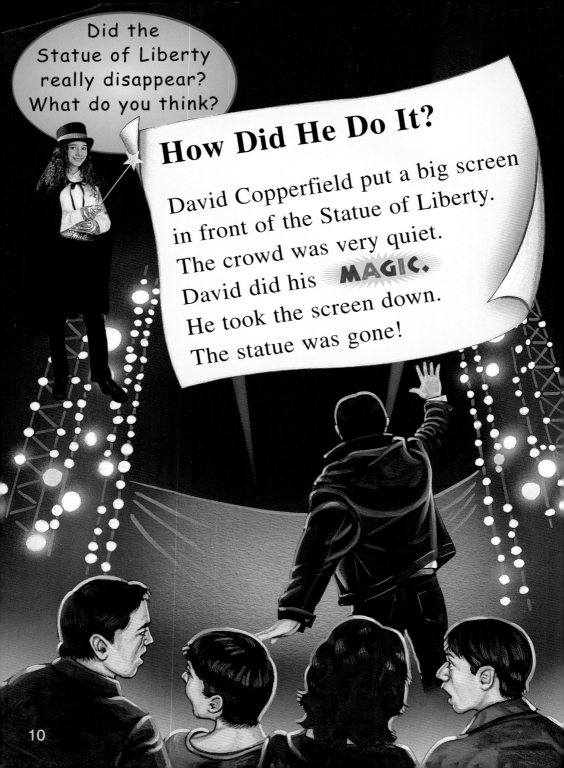

Did the Statue of Liberty really disappear? What do you think?

How Did He Do It?

David Copperfield put a big screen in front of the Statue of Liberty. The crowd was very quiet. David did his MAGIC. He took the screen down. The statue was gone!

The crowd clapped and cheered.
Then they were very quiet again.
David put the screen back up.
He did his MAGIC.
He took the screen down again.
The Statue of Liberty was back!

When Did the Magic Start?

David Copperfield
has always liked magic.
When he was eighteen years old,
he did some magic shows on TV.

Now David Copperfield is
a magic superstar.
He has won lots of prizes
for his magic shows.

David Copperfield
does magic shows
all over the world.
His shows have
lots of music and
special effects.

David's Tricks

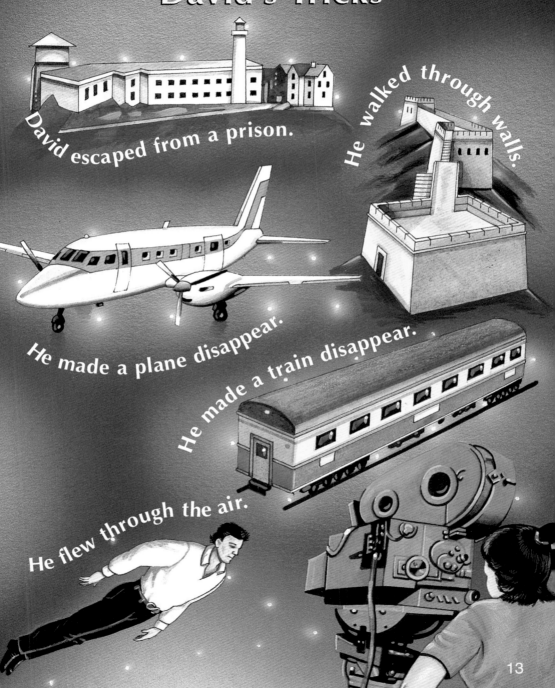

David escaped from a prison.

He walked through walls.

He made a plane disappear.

He made a train disappear.

He flew through the air.

13

Magic Museum

David Copperfield likes collecting magic tricks. He has collected so many tricks, he has started a museum. Some of the world's best magic tricks are in David's museum.

How else could magic be used to help people?

Magic's Helping Hand

Some disabled people learn David's hand tricks. Doing the tricks helps to keep their hands strong.

MAGIC TRICKS

Try these magic tricks and amaze your friends!

THE MAGIC PEPPER TRICK

To do this trick, you will need:

Water

A bowl

Black pepper

Dishwashing soap

Before you do this trick, fill the bowl with water.

Put a little dishwashing soap on your finger when no one is looking.

Step 1

Put the bowl of water on the table in front of you. Sprinkle the water with lots of black pepper. Let it stand for about ten seconds.

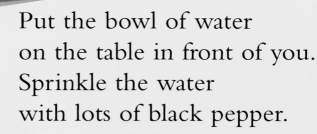

Step 2

Tell your friends
you can make the pepper move
without blowing
or stirring the water
and without moving the bowl.
Then let your friends try.
They will not be able
to make the pepper move.

A good magician
never tells how a trick
is done!

Step 3

Put your finger with
the soap on it
into the water.
The pepper will rush
to the sides of the bowl.

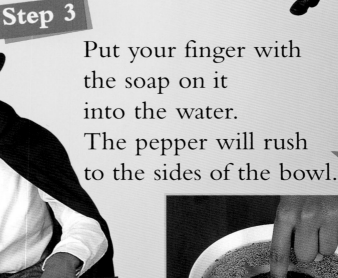

THE MAGIC KNOT TRICK

To do this trick, you will need a scarf or a large handkerchief.

Step 1

Tell your friends
you can tie a knot in the scarf
without letting go of the ends.
Let your friends try.
They will not be able to tie
a knot in the scarf
without letting go of the ends.

Step 2

Fold the scarf like this.

Practise these tricks. Then you can put on a show!

Step 3

Fold your arms across your chest. Then pick up each end of the scarf.

20

Unfold your arms
without letting go of the ends
of the scarf.

Step 5

As you unfold your arms,
the scarf will twist
into a knot!

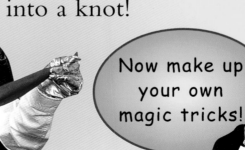

Now make up
your own
magic tricks!

21

Magical Rice

A story from Japan retold by Avelyn Davidson
Illustrated by Xiangyi Mo and Jingwen Wang

Once there was a village
where the people were never hungry.
They had lots of rice to eat.
They did not grow the rice.
The rice came to them
from a mountain near the village.

People around the world tell stories about magic.

Once a year,
giant grains of rice
rolled down the mountain
and into each house.
The people cut the rice
into little bits
and cooked them.

23

One day, a man and a woman
came to the village.
"We can't stay here,"
said the woman.
"There is no food."

Just then,
they heard a rumble.
The people ran out of their houses
and shouted,
   "Rumble once, rumble twice.
   Open your doors.
   Here comes the rice."

What other foods go well with rice?

Giant grains of rice rolled down the mountain and into each house.

25

The man and the woman
stayed in the village.
But soon the man was not happy.
He wanted more rice.
He said, "I will make another house.
If we have two houses,
we will get more rice."

"That is greedy," said the woman.
"It is bad to be greedy."

But the man didn't listen.
He made another house.
The woman said,
"Two houses are plenty.
Don't be greedy."

But the man didn't listen.
He said, "I want one more house.
Then we will have three houses.
We will get even more rice."

27

Why is
the man
angry?

Just then, they heard a rumble.
The people ran out of
their houses and shouted,
"Rumble once, rumble twice.
Open your doors.
Here comes the rice."

"Go away, go away,"
the man shouted at the rice.
"I do not want you to come yet.
My houses are not done."
He was very mad.

When a grain of rice stopped,
the man ran up to it.
He hit it with a stick again and again.
The rice broke apart and
shattered forever.

Rice never rolled
down the mountain again.
From that day on,
people had to grow
their own rice.

Can you
think of another
story where
something magical
happens?

Index